Macb

The Shorter Shakespeare

Adapted from William Shakespeare
By Christine E Shepherd

Series Editor: Tracy Irish

Contents

Cover photograph: Kate Fleetwood (as Lady Macbeth), Chichester Festival Theatre
Photo: Richard Termine

Title page photograph: Michelle O'Neill (Lady Macbeth), Guthrie Theater, © Michal Daniel

Text adaptations:

The narrators are used to summarise action and clarify events.

Certain characters, such as some thanes and the two Siwards, have been removed for the sake of both brevity and clarity, and any essential dialogue re-allocated.

Act 3 Scenes 5 and 6 have been omitted, but Scene 6 is included in the Macbeth Resource Book for those wishing to study it in detail. Act 5 Scenes 6-8 have been combined.

Where different editions give alternative versions of punctuation or disagree on whether a speech is prose or blank verse, we have chosen the more modern alternative to make for easier reading.

Character List

The Scottish Royal Family

King Duncan of Scotland

Malcolm, his elder son

Donalbain, his younger son

Scottish Lords, their families and servants

Macbeth, Thane of Glamis and Commander of the King's army

Lady Macbeth

Seyton, servant of Macbeth

Gentlewoman, Lady Macbeth's lady-in-waiting

Porter at Macbeth's castle

Doctor

Banquo, a thane, also Commander of the King's army

Fleance, his son

Lennox, a thane

Ross, a thane

Macduff, Thane of Fife

Lady Macduff

Their Son

Supernatural characters

Three Witches

Three Apparitions – one an armed head, one a bloody child, one a child wearing a crown

The Ghost of Banquo

Others

Three Murderers **Servants** **Messengers**

Two Narrators

Narrator 1 usually gives information about the plot and characters.
Narrator 2 usually poses questions but sometimes comments on the scenes.
The modern text for the narrators is printed in a different typeface.

Guthrie Theater, © Michal Daniel

Act 1 Scene 1

A desolate place near Forres in Scotland

There is a howling wind. In the distance there is the sound of thunder and lightning. The two Narrators enter, huddled against the wind. They stop when they see the witches.

The thunder and lightning get closer

First Witch: When shall we three meet again?
In thunder, lightning, or in rain?

Second Witch: When the hurly-burly's done,
When the battle's lost and won.

Third Witch: That will be ere the set of sun.

First Witch: Where the place?

Second Witch: Upon the heath.

Third Witch: There to meet with Macbeth.

All: Fair is foul, and foul is fair,
Hover through the fog and filthy air.

They leave

Narrator 1: It's OK. They've gone.

Narrator 2: What on earth were those?

Narrator 1: Witches. Three witches. They were meeting to talk about Macbeth.

Narrator 2: Macbeth? Who is Macbeth?

Narrator 1: A great Thane of Scotland.

Narrator 2: What's a Thane?

Narrator 1: A Lord. Macbeth is Thane of Glamis. He's brave, fearless and loyal. At the moment he is fighting for his king, King Duncan.There's been a rebellion. Some other Scottish thanes have turned traitors. Macbeth and Banquo are the Commanders of the King's army. It is their job to deal with the traitors.

Narrator 2: *(As they leave)* But why would those witches want to speak to him?

Act 1 Scene 2

King Duncan's military camp, near the royal castle at Forres.

King Duncan and Ross, one of his Thanes, are talking.
The Narrators enter.

Narrator 1: King Duncan is also discussing Macbeth.

Narrator 2: What's being said?

Narrator 1: Well, he's hearing from one of his lords how the battle has been won, mainly because of the bravery of Macbeth and his friend Banquo.

Narrator 2: King Duncan must be grateful to Macbeth.

Narrator 1: He certainly is. In fact he's decided to give him another title and the extra lands and money that go with it.

Narrator 2: What new title will Macbeth get?

Narrator 1: Thane of Cawdor.

Narrator 2: But isn't there a Thane of Cawdor already?

Narrator 1: Not for much longer! He was one of the chief traitors, so Duncan is having him put to death.

King Duncan: No more that Thane of Cawdor shall deceive
Our bosom interest. Go pronounce his present death,
And with his former title greet Macbeth.

Ross: I'll see it done.

King Duncan: What he hath lost, noble Macbeth hath won.

Ross and the King go out in different directions.

The Narrators leave together

Act 1 Scene 3

A desolate place near Forres

The three witches enter talking to each other. There is a roll of thunder which changes into the beat of drum

Third Witch: A drum! A drum!
Macbeth doth come.

Three Witches: The weird sisters hand in hand,
Posters of the sea and land,
Thus do go about, about,
Thrice to thine, and thrice to mine,
And thrice again, to make up nine.
Peace! The charm's wound up.

Macbeth and Banquo come in

Macbeth: So foul and fair a day I have not seen.

Banquo: How far is't called to Forres? What are these,
So withered, and so wild in their attire,
That look not like th' inhabitants o' th' earth
And yet are on't? Live you, or are you aught
That man may question? You seem to understand me
By each at once her choppy finger laying
Upon her skinny lips.

Macbeth: *(To the Witches)* Speak, if you can. What are you?

First Witch: All hail, Macbeth! Hail to thee, Thane of Glamis.

Second Witch: All hail, Macbeth! Hail to thee, Thane of Cawdor.

Third Witch: All hail, Macbeth, that shalt be king hereafter!

Banquo: *(To Macbeth)* Good sir, why do you start and seem to fear
Things that do sound so fair?
(To the Witches) I' th' name of truth,
Are ye fantastical or that indeed
Which outwardly ye show? My noble partner
You greet with present grace and great prediction
Of noble having and of royal hope,
That he seems rapt[1] withal. To me you speak not.

---

[1] totally absorbed

Liam Brennan as Macbeth with the weird sisters, Royal Lyceum Theatre, Edinburgh. Photo: Douglas McBride

If you can look into the seeds of time
And say which grain will grow and which will not,
Speak then to me, who neither beg nor fear
Your favours nor your hate.

First Witch: Hail!

Second Witch: Hail!

Third Witch: Hail!

First Witch: Lesser than Macbeth, and greater.

Second Witch: Not so happy, yet much happier.

Third Witch: Thou shalt get[1] kings, though thou be none.
So all hail, Macbeth and Banquo!

First Witch: Banquo and Macbeth, all hail!

Macbeth: Stay, you imperfect speakers, tell me more.
By Sinel's[2] death I know I am Thane of Glamis,
But how of Cawdor? The Thane of Cawdor lives,
A prosperous gentleman, and to be king
Stands not within the prospect of belief,
No more than to be Cawdor. Say from whence
You owe this strange intelligence, or why
Upon this blasted heath you stop our way
With such prophetic greeting. Speak, I charge you.

The Witches vanish

Banquo: The earth hath bubbles, as the water has,
And these are of them. Whither are they vanished?

Macbeth: Into the air, and what seemed corporal[3] melted,
As breath into the wind. Would they had stayed.

Banquo: Were such things here as we do speak about,
Or have we eaten on the insane root
That takes the reason prisoner?

Macbeth: Your children shall be kings.

Banquo: You shall be king.

Macbeth: And Thane of Cawdor too. Went it not so?

---

[1] be the father of [2] Macbeth's father [3] physical

Banquo: To th' self-same tune and words. Who's here?

Ross and another Lord enter

Ross: The King hath happily received, Macbeth,
The news of thy success. As thick as hail
Came post with post, and every one did bear
Thy praises in his kingdom's great defence.
And, for an earnest of a greater honour,
He bade me from him call thee Thane of Cawdor,
In which addition, hail, most worthy thane,
For it is thine.

Banquo: What, can the devil speak true?

Macbeth: The Thane of Cawdor lives. Why do you dress me
In borrowed robes?

Ross: Who was the thane lives yet,
But under heavy judgement bears that life
Which he deserves to lose.

Macbeth: *(To himself)* Glamis, and Thane of Cawdor. The
greatest is behind.
(To Banquo) Do you not hope your children shall be kings
When those that gave the Thane of Cawdor to me
Promised no less to them?

Banquo: That, trusted home,
Might yet enkindle you unto the crown,
Besides the Thane of Cawdor. But 'tis strange,
And oftentimes to win us to our harm
The instruments of darkness tell us truths,
Win us with honest trifles to betray 's
In deepest consequence.
(To Ross) Cousin, a word, I pray you.

Macbeth: *(To himself)* Two truths are told
As happy prologues to the swelling act
Of the imperial theme. – I thank you gentlemen –
This supernatural soliciting[1]
Cannot be ill, cannot be good. If ill,
Why hath it given me earnest of success

---

[1] persuasion

Commencing in a truth? I am Thane of Cawdor.
If good, why do I yield to that suggestion
Whose horrid image doth unfix my hair
And make my seated heart knock at my ribs
Against the use of nature?

Banquo: *(To Ross)* Look how our partner's rapt.

Macbeth: If chance will have me king, why, chance may crown me
Without my stir.

Banquo: New honours come upon him,
Like our strange garments, cleave not to their mould
But with the aid of use.

Macbeth: *(To himself)* Come what come may,
Time and the hour runs through the roughest day.

Banquo: Worthy Macbeth, we stay upon your leisure.

Macbeth: Give me your favour. My dull brain was wrought
With things forgotten. Let us toward the King.

He draws Banquo aside to speak to him.

Think upon what hath chanced, and at more time,
The interim having weighed it, let us speak
Our free hearts each to other.

Banquo: Very gladly.

Macbeth: Till then, enough. Come, friends.

They go out.

Act 1 Scene 4

King Duncan's palace at Forres

The two Narrators come in.

Narrator 2: The witches have promised an awful lot to Macbeth. Do you think he should believe them?

Narrator 1: Well, the first promise has come true. Macbeth is Thane of Cawdor.

Narrator 2: Oh, yes. The previous Thane of Cawdor has just been executed.

Narrator 1: And the King has made another decision. He's decided to make his son, Malcolm, Prince of Cumberland.

Narrator 2: What does that mean?

Narrator 1: It's a sign that Malcolm will be the next king.

Narrator 2: But didn't the witches say Macbeth was going to be king?

Narrator 1: Be quiet and watch

Narrator 1 leads Narrator 2 aside.

King Duncan enters, with his sons Malcolm and Donalbain, some lords and their servants.

King Duncan: Is execution done on Cawdor?

Malcolm: My liege,
They are not yet come back. But I have spoke
With one that saw him die, who did report
That very frankly he confessed his treasons,
Implored your highness' pardon, and set forth
A deep repentance. Nothing in his life
Became him like the leaving it.

King Duncan: There's no art
To find the mind's construction in the face.
He was a gentleman on whom I built
An absolute trust.

Macbeth, Banquo and Ross come in.

King Duncan: *(To Macbeth)* O worthiest cousin,
The sin of my ingratitude even now
Was heavy on me. Only I have left to say,
More is thy due than more than all can pay

Macbeth: The service and the loyalty I owe,
In doing it, pays itself. Your highness' part
Is to receive our duties, and our duties
Are to your throne and state, children and servants.

King Duncan: Welcome hither.
I have begun to plant thee, and will labour
To make thee full of growing. Noble Banquo,

That hast no less deserved, nor must be known
No less to have done so, let me enfold thee
And hold thee to my heart.

Banquo: There if I grow
The harvest is your own.

King Duncan: My plenteous joys,
Wanton in fullness, seek to hide themselves
In drops of sorrow. Sons, kinsmen, thanes,
And you whose places are the nearest, know
We will establish our estate upon
Our eldest, Malcolm, whom we name hereafter
The Prince of Cumberland; which honour must
Not unaccompanied invest him only,
But signs of nobleness, like stars, shall shine
On all deservers.
(To Macbeth) From hence to Inverness,
And bind us further to you.

Macbeth: I'll be myself the harbinger,[1] and make joyful
The hearing of my wife with your approach;
So humbly take my leave.

King Duncan: My worthy Cawdor.

As Macbeth moves away, the King turns to Banquo and starts to talk to him.

Macbeth: *(To himself)* The Prince of Cumberland–that is a step
On which I must fall down or else o'erleap,
For in my way it lies. Stars, hide your fires,
Let not light see my black and deep desires;
The eye wink at the hand; yet let that be,
Which the eye fears, when it is done, to see.

Macbeth leaves in one direction, the King and all the rest in another.

[1] someone sent in advance to prepare

Act 1 Scene 5

Macbeth's castle at Inverness

Lady Macbeth comes in, reading a letter from Macbeth

Lady Macbeth: *(Reading)* "They met me in the day of success, and I have learned they have more in them than mortal knowledge. When I burned in desire to question them further, they vanished. Whiles I stood rapt in the wonder of it came missives from the King, who all-hailed me Thane of Cawdor, by which title before these weird sisters saluted me, and referred me to the coming on of time with 'Hail, King that shalt be!' This have I thought good to deliver thee, my dearest partner of greatness, that thou mightst not lose the dues of rejoicing by being ignorant of what greatness is promised thee. Lay it to thy heart, and farewell."

Glamis thou art, and Cawdor, and shalt be
What thou art promised. Yet do I fear thy nature.
It is too full o' th' milk of human kindness
To catch the nearest way. Thou wouldst be great,
Art not without ambition, but without
The illness should attend it. Hie thee hither,
That I may pour my spirits in thine ear
And chastise with the valour of my tongue
All that impedes thee from the golden round
Which fate and metaphysical aid doth seem
To have thee crowned withal.
A servant comes in
What is your tidings?

Servant: The King comes here tonight.

Lady Macbeth: Thou'rt mad to say it.

Servant: So please you, it is true. Our thane is coming,
One of my fellows had the speed of him.

Lady Macbeth: He brings great news.
Lady Macbeth sends the servant away

The raven himself is hoarse
That croaks the fatal entrance of Duncan
Under my battlements. Come, you spirits
That tend on mortal thoughts, unsex me here,
And fill me from the crown to the toe top-full
Of direst cruelty. Make thick my blood,
Stop up th' access and passage to remorse,
Come to my woman's breasts,
And take my milk for gall, you murd'ring ministers,
Wherever in your sightless substances
You wait on nature's mischief. Come, thick night,
And pall thee in the dunnest[1] smoke of hell,
That my keen knife see not the wound it makes,
Nor heaven peep through the blanket of the dark
To cry "Hold, hold!" *(Macbeth enters)*
Great Glamis, worthy Cawdor,
Greater than both by the all-hail hereafter,
Thy letters have transported me beyond
This ignorant present, and I feel now
The future in the instant.

Macbeth: My dearest love, Duncan comes here tonight.

Lady Macbeth: And when goes hence?

Macbeth: Tomorrow, as he purposes.

Lady Macbeth: O never shall sun that morrow see.
Your face, my thane, is as a book where men
May read strange matters. To beguile[2] the time,
Look like the time; bear welcome in your eye,
Your hand, your tongue; look like the innocent flower,
But be the serpent under 't. He that's coming
Must be provided for; and you shall put
This night's great business into my dispatch.

Macbeth: We will speak further.

Lady Macbeth: Only look up clear.
To alter favour ever is to fear.
Leave all the rest to me.

They leave together

[1] darkest [2] trick, deceive

Michelle O'Neill (as Lady Macbeth) and Erik Heger (as Macbeth), Guthrie Theater, © Michal Daniel

Act 1 Scene 6

Outside Macbeth's castle

Music is being played and lights being brought in.

King Duncan comes in with his sons, Malcolm and Donalbain, and Banquo, Macduff, Ross, various Lords and their servants.

King Duncan: This castle hath a pleasant seat. The air
Nimbly and sweetly recommends itself
Unto our gentle senses.

Lady Macbeth comes out to greet them

King Duncan: See, see, our honoured hostess!

Lady Macbeth: All our service
In every point twice done, and then done double,
Were poor and single business to contend
Against those honours deep and broad wherewith
Your majesty loads our house.

King Duncan: Where's the Thane of Cawdor? He rides well,
And his great love, sharp as his spur, hath holp him
To his home before us. Fair and noble hostess,
We are your guest tonight. Give me your hand.
Conduct me to mine host. We love him highly,
And shall continue our graces towards him.
By your leave, hostess.

They enter the castle

Act 1 Scene 7

A room near the Great Hall in Macbeth's castle

There is music and noise, people bringing dishes for the feast. Macbeth comes in.

Macbeth: If it were done when 'tis done, then 'twere well
It were done quickly. That but this blow
Might be the be-all and the end-all, here,
But here, upon this bank and shoal of time,
We'd jump the life to come. But in these cases,

We still have judgement here, that we but teach
Bloody instructions which, being taught, return
To plague th' inventor. This even-handed justice
Commends th' ingredients of our poisoned chalice
To our own lips. He's here in double trust:
First, as I am his kinsman and his subject,
Strong both against the deed; then, as his host,
Who should against his murderer shut the door,
Not bear the knife myself. Besides, this Duncan
Hath borne his faculties so meek, hath been
So clear in his great office, that his virtues
Will plead like angels, trumpet-tongued
And pity, like a naked new-born babe,
Shall blow the horrid deed in every eye
That tears shall drown the wind. I have no spur
To prick the sides of my intent, but only
Vaulting ambition which o'erleaps itself
And falls on th' other.

Lady Macbeth comes in

Macbeth: How now? What news?

Lady Macbeth: He has almost supped. Why have you left the chamber?

Macbeth: Hath he asked for me?

Lady Macbeth: Know you not he has?

Macbeth: We will proceed no further in this business.
He hath honoured me of late, and I have bought
Golden opinions from all sorts of people,
Which would be worn now in their newest gloss,
Not cast aside so soon.

Lady Macbeth: Was the hope drunk
Wherein you dressed yourself? Hath it slept since?
And wakes it now to look so green and pale
At what it did so freely? From this time
Such I account thy love. Art thou afeard
To be the same in thine own act and valour
As thou art in desire? Wouldst thou have that

Which thou esteem'st the ornament of life,
And live a coward in thine own esteem?

Macbeth: Prithee, peace.
I dare do all that may become a man;
Who dares do more is none.

Lady Macbeth: What beast was 't then
That made you break this enterprise to me?
When you durst do it, then you were a man;
And to be more than what you were, you would
Be so much more the man.
I have given suck, and know
How tender 'tis to love the babe that milks me.
I would, while it was smiling in my face,
Have plucked my nipple from his boneless gums
And dashed the brains out, had I so sworn
As you have done to this.

Macbeth: If we should fail?

Lady Macbeth: We fail?
But screw your courage to the sticking-place,
And we'll not fail. When Duncan is asleep,
Whereto the rather shall his day's hard journey
Soundly invite him, his two chamberlains
Will I with wine and wassail so convince
That memory, the warder of the brain,
Shall be a fume. When in swinish sleep
Their drenchèd natures lie as in a death,
What cannot you and I perform upon
Th' unguarded Duncan? What not put upon
His spongy officers, who shall bear the guilt
Of our great quell?

Macbeth: Bring forth men-children only,
For thy undaunted mettle should compose
Nothing but males. Will it not be received,
When we have marked with blood those sleepy two
Of his own chamber and used their very daggers,
That they have done 't?

Lady Macbeth: Who dares receive it other,
As we shall make our griefs and clamour roar
Upon his death?

Macbeth: I am settled, and bend up
Each corporal agent to this terrible feat.
Away, and mock the time with fairest show.
False face must hide what the false heart doth know.

They go out

Michelle O'Neill (as Lady Macbeth) and Erik Heger (as Macbeth),
Guthrie Theater, © Michal Daniel

Act 2 Scene 1

The Courtyard of Macbeth's castle

The two Narrators enter. Banquo and his son, Fleance, come in talking quietly to each other.

Narrator 1: Everything's quiet now at Macbeth's castle. Most people have gone to bed. Banquo and his son, Fleance have been walking and talking.

Narrator 2: Do you think Banquo suspects anything?

Narrator 1: He might, but King Duncan doesn't, he's very pleased with his welcome.

Narrator 2: Look, Macbeth's awake too.

Macbeth comes in with a servant who is carrying a torch

Banquo:: Give me my sword. Who's there?

Macbeth: A friend.

Banquo: What, sir, not yet at rest? The King's a-bed.
He hath been in unusual pleasure.
This diamond he greets your wife withal
By the name of most kind hostess.

He pauses for a moment.

I dreamed last night of the three weird sisters.
To you they have showed some truth.

Macbeth: I think not of them;
Yet, when we can entreat an hour to serve,
We would spend it in some words upon that business
If you would grant the time.

Banquo: At your kind'st leisure.

Macbeth: Good repose the while.

Banquo: Thanks, sir. The like to you.

Banquo and Fleance go out as Macbeth speaks to the servant

Macbeth: Go bid thy mistress, when my drink is ready,
She strike upon the bell. Get thee to bed.

The servant leaves. Macbeth becomes very thoughtful.

Hull Truck Theatre. Photo: Louise Buckby

Alec Baldwin as Macbeth, Public Theater, New York. Photo: Michal Daniel

Is this a dagger which I see before me,
The handle toward my hand? Come, let me clutch thee.
I have thee not, and yet I see thee still.
Art thou not, fatal vision, sensible
To feeling as to sight? Or art thou but
A dagger of the mind, a false creation,
Proceeding from the heat-oppressèd brain?
I see thee yet, in form as palpable
As this which now I draw.
Thou marshall'st me the way that I was going,
And such an instrument I was to use.
Mine eyes are made the fools o' th' other senses,
Or else worth all the rest. I see thee still,
And on thy blade and dudgeon[1] gouts of blood,
Which was not so before. There's no such thing.
It is the bloody business which informs
Thus to mine eyes. Now o'er the one half-world
Nature seems dead, and wicked dreams abuse
The curtained sleep. *(A bell rings)*
I go, and it is done. The bell invites me.
Hear it not, Duncan; for it is a knell
That summons thee to heaven or to hell.

Macbeth goes out

---

[1] handle

Act 2 Scene 2

Near Duncan's room in Macbeth's castle

The Narrators come in

Narrator 2: What was wrong with Duncan's guards? They shouldn't be sleeping on duty, should they?

Narrator 1: No, of course they shouldn't. But don't you remember that Lady Macbeth said she was going to get them drunk and sleepy.

Narrator 2: She's here, she's here! She looks really frightening. Let's go!

The Narrators leave quickly as Lady Macbeth comes in.

Lady Macbeth: That which hath made them drunk hath made me bold.
What hath quenched them hath given me fire.

There is the sound of a screech.

Hark, peace!
It was the owl that shrieked, the fatal bellman
Which gives the stern'st good-night. He is about it.
The doors are open, and the surfeited[1] grooms
Do mock their charge with snores. I have drugged their possets,[2]
That death and nature do contend about them
Whether they live or die.

Macbeth: *(From offstage)* Who's there? What, ho?

Lady Macbeth: Alack, I am afraid they have awaked,
And 'tis not done. Th' attempt and not the deed
Confounds us. Hark!—I laid their daggers ready;
He could not miss 'em. Had he not resembled
My father as he slept, I had done 't.

Macbeth comes in carrying two bloody daggers. His hands are also covered in blood.

My husband?

Macbeth: I have done the deed. Didst thou not hear a noise?

Lady Macbeth: I heard the owl scream and the crickets cry.
Did not you speak?

---

[1] drunken [2] drinks

Macbeth: When?

Lady Macbeth: Now.

Macbeth: As I descended?

Lady Macbeth: Ay.

Macbeth: *(Looking at his hands)* This is a sorry sight.

Lady Macbeth: A foolish thought, to say a sorry sight.

Macbeth: There's one did laugh in 's sleep, and one cried "Murder!"
That they did wake each other. I stood and heard them.
One cried "God bless us" and "Amen" the other,
As they had seen me with these hangman's hands.
List'ning their fear I could not say "Amen"
When they did say "God bless us."

Lady Macbeth: Consider it not so deeply.

Macbeth: But wherefore could not I pronounce "Amen"?
I had most need of blessing, and "Amen"
Stuck in my throat.

Lady Macbeth: These deeds must not be thought
After these ways; so, it will make us mad.

Macbeth: Methought I heard a voice cry "Sleep no more,
Macbeth does murder sleep"—the innocent sleep,
Sleep that knits up the ravelled[1] sleeve of care,
The death of each day's life, sore labour's bath,
Balm of hurt minds, great nature's second course,
Chief nourisher in life's feast—

Lady Macbeth: What do you mean?

Macbeth: Still it cried "Sleep no more" to all the house,
"Glamis hath murdered sleep, and therefore Cawdor
Shall sleep no more, Macbeth shall sleep no more."

Lady Macbeth: Who was it that thus cried? Why, worthy thane,
You do unbend your noble strength to think
So brain-sickly of things. Go get some water
And wash this filthy witness from your hand.
Why did you bring these daggers from the place?
They must lie there. Go, carry them, and smear
The sleepy grooms with blood.

---

[1] tangled, frayed

Michelle O'Neill (as Lady Macbeth) and Erik Heger (as Macbeth), Guthrie Theater, © Michal Daniel

Macbeth: I'll go no more.
I am afraid to think what I have done,
Look on 't again I dare not.

Lady Macbeth: Infirm of purpose!
Give me the daggers. The sleeping and the dead
Are but as pictures. 'Tis the eye of childhood
That fears a painted devil. If he do bleed
I'll gild the faces of the grooms withal,
For it must seem their guilt.

She goes out with the daggers.

There is the sound of knocking.

Macbeth: Whence is that knocking?—
How is 't with me when every noise appals me?
What hands are here! Ha, they pluck out mine eyes.
Will all great Neptune's ocean wash this blood
Clean from my hand? No, this my hand will rather
The multitudinous seas incarnadine,
Making the green one red.

Lady Macbeth returns. Her hands are covered in blood

Lady Macbeth: My hands are of your colour, but I shame
To wear a heart so white.

There is the sound of knocking again

I hear a knocking
At the south entry. Retire we to our chamber.
A little water clears us of this deed.
How easy is it then!

Once again, there is the sound of knocking

Hark, more knocking.
Get on your nightgown, lest occasion call us
And show us to be watchers. Be not lost
So poorly in your thoughts.

Macbeth: To know my deed 'twere best not know myself.

There is the sound of more knocking

Wake Duncan with thy knocking! I would thou couldst.

They go out.

Act 2 Scene 3

The gate of Macbeth's castle

There is the sound of loud knocking. The Porter comes in.

Porter: Here's a knocking indeed! If a man were porter of hell-gate he should have old turning the key. Knock, knock, knock. Who's there, i' th' name of Beelzebub? Knock, knock. Never at quiet. But this place is too cold for hell. I'll devil-porter it no further.

He opens the gate. Macduff and Lennox come in.

Macduff: Was it so late, friend, ere you went to bed
That you do lie so late?

Porter: Faith, sir, we were carousing till the second cock.

Macduff: Is thy master stirring?
Our knocking has awaked him: here he comes.

Macbeth comes in and the Porter leaves.

Lennox: *(To Macbeth)* Good morrow, noble sir.

Macbeth: Good morrow, both.

Macduff: Is the King stirring, worthy thane?

Macbeth: Not yet.

Macduff: He did command me to call timely on him.
I have almost slipped the hour.

Macbeth: I'll bring you to him.

Macduff: I'll make so bold to call.

Macduff goes out towards King Duncan's room.

Lennox: Goes the King hence today?

Macbeth: He does – he did appoint so.

Lennox: The night has been unruly, where we lay,
Lamentings heard i' th' air, strange screams of death,
And prophesying with accents terrible
Of dire combustion and confused events.
Some say the earth was feverous and did shake.

Macbeth: 'Twas a rough night.

Macduff rushes back in.

Macduff: O, horror, horror, horror!
Tongue nor heart cannot conceive nor name thee.

Macbeth & Lennox: What's the matter?

Macduff: Confusion now hath made his masterpiece.
Most sacrilegious[1] murder hath broke ope
The Lord's anointed temple and stole thence
The life o' th' building.

Macbeth: What is 't you say—the life?

Lennox: Mean you his majesty?

Macduff: Approach the chamber. Do not bid me speak.
See, and then speak yourselves.

Macbeth and Lennox hurry out.

Macduff: Awake, awake!
Ring the alarum bell. Murder and treason!
Banquo and Donalbain! Malcolm, awake!
Shake off this downy sleep, death's counterfeit,
And look on death itself. Malcolm, Banquo,
As from your graves rise up, and walk like sprites
To countenance this horror.

A bell rings. Lady Macbeth comes in.

Lady Macbeth: What's the business,
That such a hideous trumpet calls to parley
The sleepers of the house? Speak, speak.

Macduff: O gentle lady,
'Tis not for you to hear what I can speak.
The repetition in a woman's ear
Would murder as it fell.

Banquo comes in

Macduff: O Banquo, Banquo,
Our royal master's murdered!

---

[1] offending against religion

Lady Macbeth: Woe, alas!
What, in our house?

Banquo: Too cruel anywhere.
Dear Duff, I prithee contradict thyself,
And say it is not so.

Macbeth and Lennox return

Macbeth: Had I but died an hour before this chance
I had lived a blessèd time, for from this instant
There's nothing serious in mortality.
All is but toys. Renown and grace is dead.

Malcolm and Donalbain come in.

Donalbain: What is amiss?

Macbeth: You are, and do not know 't.
The spring, the head, the fountain of your blood
Is stopped, the very source of it is stopped.

Macduff: Your royal father's murdered.

Malcolm: O, by whom?

Lennox: Those of his chamber, as it seemed, had done 't.
Their hands and faces were all badged with blood,
So were their daggers, which, unwiped, we found
Upon their pillows. They stared and were distracted.
No man's life was to be trusted with them.

Macbeth: O, yet I do repent me of my fury
That I did kill them.

Macduff: Wherefore did you so?

Macbeth: Who can be wise, amazed, temperate and furious,
Loyal and neutral, in a moment? No man.
Th' expedition of my violent love
Outran the pauser, reason. Here lay Duncan,
His silver skin laced with his golden blood,
And his gashed stabs looked like a breach in nature
For ruin's wasteful entrance. There the murderers,
Steeped in the colours of their trade, their daggers
Unmannerly breeched with gore. Who could refrain,

Allison McKenzie as Lady Macbeth, Royal Lyceum Theatre, Edinburgh. Photo: Douglas McBride

That had a heart to love, and in that heart
Courage to make 's love known?

Lady Macbeth: Help me hence, ho!

Macduff: Look to the lady.

Lady Macbeth is helped out. Malcolm and Donalbain speak quietly to each other while this is going on.

Malcolm: Why do we hold our tongues,
That most may claim this argument for ours?

Donalbain: What should be spoken here?
Let's away. Our tears are not yet brewed.

Malcolm: Nor our strong sorrow upon the foot of motion.

Banquo: Look to the lady;
And when we have our naked frailties hid,
That suffer in exposure, let us meet
And question this most bloody piece of work
To know it further.

Macbeth: Let's briefly put on manly readiness,
And meet i' th' hall together.

Everyone leaves except Malcolm and Donalbain

Malcolm: What will you do? Let's not consort with them.
To show an unfelt sorrow is an office
Which the false man does easy. I'll to England.

Donalbain: To Ireland, I. Our separated fortune
Shall keep us both the safer. Where we are
There's daggers in men's smiles. The nearer in blood,
The nearer bloody.

Malcolm: This murderous shaft that's shot
Hath not yet lighted, and our safest way
Is to avoid the aim. Therefore to horse,
And let us not be dainty of leave-taking,
But shift away.

They leave.

Act 2 Scene 4

Outside Macbeth's castle

The Narrators come in

Narrator 2: There's been a lot of rumours about strange and unnatural happenings. And there seems to be a lot of suspicion.

Narrator 1: Yes, Donalbain and Malcolm don't trust anyone. That's why Donalbain's gone to Ireland and Malcolm's fled to England.

Narrator 2: I thought that Malcolm was supposed to be the next king of Scotland.

Narrator 1: That was King Duncan's wish, but things have changed now, Macbeth has been named king.

Ross and Macduff come in talking to each other

Ross: Is 't known who did this more than bloody deed?

Macduff: Those that Macbeth hath slain.

Ross: Alas the day,
What good could they pretend?

Macduff: They were suborned.[1]
Malcolm and Donalbain, the King's two sons,
Are stol'n away and fled, which puts upon them
Suspicion of the deed.

Ross: 'Gainst nature still. Then 'tis most like
The sovereignty will fall upon Macbeth.

Macduff: He is already named and gone to Scone
To be invested.

Ross: Will you to Scone?

Macduff: No, cousin, I'll to Fife.

Ross: Well, I will thither.

Macduff: Well, may you see things well done there. Adieu,
Lest our old robes sit easier than our new.

They leave in opposite directions to each other.

---

[1] bribed

Act 3 Scene 1

The royal palace at Forres

The Narrators come in.

Narrator 2: So the witches' prophecies have come true?

Narrator 1: Yes, Macbeth has been to Scone to be crowned. But Macduff is not happy about it. He went home to his castle in Fife instead of to the coronation.

Narrator 2: Won't that make Macbeth his enemy?

Narrator 1: You're right, it will upset Macbeth.

Narrator 2: What sort of a king do you think Macbeth will be? He might be a good leader, he's brave and he's a good fighter.

Narrator 1: Yes, but he's a murderer. And he's stolen the crown, he doesn't have any right to it.

Narrator 2: What about Banquo? The witches spoke to him as well.

Narrator 1: He doesn't seem to have been influenced by them. He's here at the royal palace at Forres with his son Fleance. Now that Macbeth is King, he is holding a big celebration at the palace.

Narrator 2: Well, I hope Banquo will be alright.

Narrator 1: Why?

Narrator 2: Well, I'm just thinking about the last time we saw an important guest arrive at a castle!

The Narrators leave. Banquo comes in dressed to go riding

Banquo: Thou hast it now: King, Cawdor, Glamis, all
As the weird women promised; and I fear
Thou played'st most foully for 't. Yet it was said
It should not stand in thy posterity,
But that myself should be the root and father
Of many kings. But hush, no more.

There is a fanfare. Macbeth and Lady Macbeth come in dressed as a King and Queen, with Ross, other Lords and servants.

Macbeth: Here's our chief guest.

Lady Macbeth: If he had been forgotten
It had been as a gap in our great feast,
And all-thing unbecoming.

Macbeth: *(to Banquo)* Tonight we hold a solemn supper, sir,
And I'll request your presence.

Banquo: Let your highness command upon me.

Macbeth: Ride you this afternoon?

Banquo: Ay, my good lord.

Macbeth: We should have else desired your good advice.
Is 't far you ride?

Banquo: As far, my lord, as will fill up the time
'Twixt this and supper.

Macbeth: Fail not our feast.

Banquo: My lord, I will not.

Macbeth: We hear our bloody cousins are bestowed
In England and in Ireland, not confessing
Their cruel parricide,[1] filling their hearers
With strange invention. But of that tomorrow.
Hie you to horse, adieu. Goes Fleance with you?

Banquo: Ay, my good lord. Our time does call upon 's.

Macbeth: I wish your horses swift and sure of foot,
Farewell. *(Banquo leaves)*
Let every man be master of his time
Till seven at night. To make society
The sweeter welcome, we will keep ourself
Till supper-time alone. While then, God be with you.

They all leave except Macbeth and a Servant

Sirrah, a word with you. Attend those men
Our pleasure?

Servant: They are, my lord, without the palace gate.

Macbeth: Bring them before us. *(The Servant leaves)*

---

[1] murder of a father

Erik Heger as Macbeth, Guthrie Theater, © Michal Daniel

Macbeth: To be thus is nothing
But to be safely thus. Our fears in Banquo
Stick deep, and in his royalty of nature
Reigns that which would be feared. 'Tis much he dares,
And to that dauntless temper of his mind
He hath a wisdom that doth guide his valour
To act in safety. There is none but he
Whose being I do fear. He chid[1] the sisters
When first they put the name of king upon me,
And bade them speak to him. Then, prophet-like,
They hailed him father to a line of kings.
Upon my head they placed a fruitless crown,
And put a barren[2] sceptre in my grip,
No son of mine succeeding. If 't be so,
For Banquo's issue have I filed[3] my mind,
For them the gracious Duncan have I murdered,
Put rancours[4] in the vessel of my peace
Only for them, and mine eternal jewel
Given to the common enemy[5] of man
To make them kings, the seeds of Banquo kings.
Who's there?

---

[1] scolded, told off [2] childless [3] defiled, spoiled [4] bitterness [5] the devil

The two Murderers come in

Macbeth: Have you considered of my speeches? Know that it was he in the times past which held you so under fortune, which you thought had been our innocent self.

1st Murderer: You made it known to us.

Macbeth: Do you find your patience so predominant in your nature that you can let this go?

2nd Murderer: I am one, my liege,
Whom the vile blows and buffets of the world
Hath so incensed that I am reckless what
I do to spite the world.

1st Murderer: And I another,
So weary with disasters, tugged with fortune,
That I would set my life on any chance
To mend it or be rid on 't.

Commonwealth Shakespeare Company, © Ryan Maxwell

Macbeth: Both of you
Know Banquo was your enemy.

Murderers: True, my lord.

Macbeth: So is he mine, and though I could
With barefaced power sweep him from my sight
And bid my will avouch it, yet I must not,
For certain friends that are both his and mine,
Whose loves I may not drop.

2nd Murderer: We shall, my lord,
Perform what you command us.

Macbeth: Your spirits shine through you. Within this hour at most
I will advise you where to plant yourselves,
Fleance, his son, that keeps him company—
Whose absence is no less material to me
Than is his father's—must embrace the fate
Of that dark hour.

Murderers: We are resolved, my lord.

The Murderers leave

Macbeth: It is concluded. Banquo, thy soul's flight,
If it find heaven, must find it out tonight.

Macbeth leaves

Act 3 Scene 2

A room in the palace

The Narrators come in.

Narrator 2: Is Macbeth really planning to kill Banquo, his best friend?

Narrator1: Yes. He can't bear the thought that Banquo's descendants will be kings and not his own children.

Narrator 2: So that's why Fleance has to be killed as well! Here's Lady Macbeth again. She doesn't look as frightening as usual.

Narrator1: And she looks very unhappy!

The narrators leave as Lady Macbeth comes in

Lady Macbeth: Nought's had, all's spent,
Where our desire is got without content.
'Tis safer to be that which we destroy
Than by destruction dwell in doubtful joy.

Macbeth comes in

How now, my lord, why do you keep alone,
Of sorriest fancies your companions making,
Using those thoughts which should indeed have died
With them they think on? Things without all remedy
Should be without regard. What's done is done.

Macbeth: We have scorched the snake, not killed it.
She'll close and be herself, whilst our poor malice
Remains in danger of her former tooth.
But let the frame of things disjoint, both the worlds suffer,
Ere we will eat our meal in fear, and sleep
In the affliction of these terrible dreams
That shake us nightly. Better be with the dead,
Whom we to gain our peace have sent to peace,
Than on the torture of the mind to lie
In restless ecstasy. Duncan is in his grave.
After life's fitful fever he sleeps well.
Treason has done his worst. Nor steel nor poison,
Malice domestic, foreign levy, nothing
Can touch him further.

Lady Macbeth: Come on, gentle my lord,
Sleek o'er your rugged looks, be bright and jovial
Among your guests tonight.

Macbeth: So shall I, love,
And so I pray be you. Let your remembrance
Apply to Banquo. Present him eminence
Both with eye and tongue; unsafe the while that we
Must lave our honours in these flattering streams
And make our faces visors to our hearts,
Disguising what they are.

Lady Macbeth: You must leave this.

Patrick Stewart (as Macbeth) and Kate Fleetwood (as Lady Macbeth), Chichester Festival Theatre.
Photo: Richard Termine

Macbeth: O, full of scorpions is my mind, dear wife!
Thou know'st that Banquo and his Fleance lives.

Lady Macbeth: But in them nature's copy's not eterne.

Macbeth: There's comfort yet, they are assailable.
Then be thou jocund[1]. Ere the bat hath flown
His cloistered flight, there shall be done
A deed of dreadful note.

Lady Macbeth: What's to be done?

Macbeth: Be innocent of the knowledge, dearest chuck,
Till thou applaud the deed. Come, seeling night,
Scarf up the tender eye of pitiful day,
And with thy bloody and invisible hand
Cancel and tear to pieces that great bond
Which keeps me pale. Light thickens, and the crow
Makes wing to th' rooky wood.
Good things of day begin to droop and drowse,
Whiles night's black agents to their preys do rouse.
Thou marvell'st at my words; but hold thee still.
Things bad begun make strong themselves by ill.
So prithee go with me.

They leave

Act 3 Scene 3

A lonely place near the palace

Three Murderers come in

1st Murderer: *(to 3rd Murderer)* But who did bid thee join with us?

3rd Murderer: Macbeth.

2nd Murderer: He needs not our mistrust, since he delivers
Our offices and what we have to do
To the direction just.

1st Murderer: *(to 3rd Murderer)* Then stand with us.

3rd Murderer: Hark, I hear horses.

Banquo: *(Out of sight)* Give us a light there, ho!

---

[1] cheerful

(Enter Banquo and Fleance with a torch)

2nd Murderer: A light, a light.

3rd Murderer: 'Tis he.

1st Murderer: Stand to 't.

Banquo: It will be rain tonight.

1st Murderer: Let it come down.

The 1st Murderer puts out the torch. The others attack Banquo

Banquo: O, treachery!
Fly, good Fleance, fly, fly, fly!

3rd Murderer: Who did strike out the light?

1st Murderer: Was 't not the way?

3rd Murderer: There's but one down. The son is fled.

2nd Murderer: We have lost best half of our affair.

1st Murderer: Well, let's away and say how much is done.

They go out, taking Banquo's body with them

Act 3 Scene 4

The banqueting hall in the palace

There is a banquet laid out and two thrones on the stage. Macbeth and Lady Macbeth come in dressed in their royal robes, with Ross, Lennox and other Lords and Servants. Lady Macbeth sits on one of the thrones. The Narrators are amongst the servants.

Macbeth: You know your own degrees; sit down. At first and last the hearty welcome.

Lords: Thanks to your majesty.

Macbeth: Ourself will mingle with society and play the humble host. Our hostess keeps her state, but in best time we will require her welcome.

Lady Macbeth: Pronounce it for me, sir, to all our friends,
For my heart speaks they are welcome.

The 1st Murderer appears at the door

Macbeth: See, they encounter thee with their hearts' thanks.
Both sides are even. Here I'll sit, i' th' midst.
Be large in mirth. Anon we'll drink a measure
The table round.
(Macbeth goes over to the 1st Murderer) There's blood upon thy face.

1st Murderer: 'Tis Banquo's, then.

Macbeth: 'Tis better thee without than he within.
Is he dispatched?

1st Murderer: My lord, his throat is cut. That I did for him.

Macbeth: Thou art the best o' th' cut-throats. Yet he's good
That did the like for Fleance.

1st Murderer: Most royal sir, Fleance is scaped.

Macbeth: Then comes my fit again; I had else been perfect,
Whole as the marble, founded as the rock,
As broad and general as the casing air,
But now I am cabined, cribbed, confined, bound in
To saucy doubts and fears. But Banquo's safe?

1st Murderer: Ay, my good lord. Safe in a ditch he bides,
With twenty trenchèd gashes on his head,
The least a death to nature.

Macbeth: Thanks for that.
There the grown serpent lies. The worm that's fled
Hath nature that in time will venom breed,
No teeth for th' present. Get thee gone.

The 1st Murderer leaves

Lady Macbeth: My royal lord, you do not give the cheer.

The Ghost of Banquo comes in covered in blood, and sits unnoticed by anyone, in Macbeth's place

Lennox: May 't please your highness sit?

Macbeth: Here had we now our country's honour roofed
Were the graced person of our Banquo present.

Who may I rather challenge for unkindness
Than pity for mischance.

Ross: His absence, sir,
Lays blame upon his promise. Please 't your highness
To grace us with your royal company?

Macbeth: The table's full.

Lennox: Here is a place reserved, sir.

Macbeth: Where?

Lennox: Here, my good lord.

Lennox notices that Macbeth looks shocked

What is 't that moves your highness?

Macbeth: Which of you have done this?

Lords: What, my good lord?

Macbeth: *(To the Ghost)* Thou canst not say I did it. Never shake
Thy gory locks at me.

Ross: *(Standing up)* Gentlemen, rise. His highness is not well.

Lady Macbeth: *(Standing up)* Sit, worthy friends. My lord is often thus,
And hath been from his youth. Upon a thought
He will again be well. If much you note him
You shall offend him, and extend his passion.
Feed, and regard him not.
(She goes to one side to speak to Macbeth) Are you a man?

Macbeth: Ay, and a bold one, that dare look on that
Which might appal the devil.

Lady Macbeth: O proper stuff!
This is the very painting of your fear;
This is the air-drawn dagger which you said
Led you to Duncan. O, these flaws and starts!
Why do you make such faces? When all's done
You look but on a stool.

Macbeth: Prithee see there. Behold, look, lo—how say you?
(To Ghost) Why, what care I? If thou canst nod, speak, too!

The Ghost leaves

Chris Colquhoun as Banquo, Royal Exchange Theatre, © Jonathan Keenan

Lady Macbeth: What, quite unmanned in folly?

Macbeth: If I stand here, I saw him.

Lady Macbeth: Fie, for shame!

Macbeth: Blood hath been shed ere now, i' th' olden time,
Ay, and since, too, murders have been performed
Too terrible for the ear. The time has been
That, when the brains were out, the man would die,
And there an end. But now they rise again
With twenty mortal murders on their crowns,
And push us from our stools. This is more strange
Than such a murder is.

Lady Macbeth: My worthy lord,
Your noble friends do lack you.

Macbeth: I do forget.
Do not muse at me, my most worthy friends.
I have a strange infirmity which is nothing
To those that know me. Come, love and health to all,
Then I'll sit down. Give me some wine. Fill full.

Banquo's Ghost returns

Macbeth: I drink to th' general joy of th' whole table,
And to our dear friend Banquo, whom we miss.
Would he were here. To all and him we thirst,
And all to all.

Lords: Our duties, and the pledge.

As the Lords drink, Macbeth sees the Ghost

Macbeth: Avaunt, and quit my sight! Let the earth hide thee.
Thy bones are marrowless, thy blood is cold.
Thou hast no speculation in those eyes
Which thou dost glare with.

Lady Macbeth: Think of this, good peers,
But as a thing of custom. 'Tis no other;
Only it spoils the pleasure of the time.

Macbeth: What man dare, I dare.
Take any shape but that, and my firm nerves
Shall never tremble. Hence, horrible shadow,
Unreal mock'ry, hence!

The Ghost leaves

Why so, being gone,
I am a man again. Pray you sit still.

Lady Macbeth: You have displaced the mirth, broke the good meeting
With most admired disorder.

Macbeth: You make me strange
Even to the disposition that I owe,
When now I think you can behold such sights
And keep the natural ruby of your cheeks
When mine is blanched with fear.

Ross: What sights, my lord?

Lady Macbeth: I pray you, speak not. He grows worse and worse.
Question enrages him. At once, good night.
Stand not upon the order of your going,
But go at once.

Lennox: Good night, and better health
Attend his majesty.

Lady Macbeth: A kind good-night to all.

The Lords and servants leave. The Narrators remain, hidden, to one side

Macbeth: It will have blood, they say. Blood will have blood.
Stones have been known to move, and trees to speak,
Augurs and understood relations have
By maggot-pies and choughs and rooks brought forth
The secret'st man of blood. What is the night?

Lady Macbeth: Almost at odds with morning, which is which.

Macbeth: How sayst thou that Macduff denies his person
At our great bidding?

Lady Macbeth: Did you send to him, sir?

Macbeth: I hear it by the way, but I will send.
There's not a one of them but in his house
I keep a servant fee'd[1]. I will tomorrow,
And betimes I will, to the weird sisters.
More shall they speak. For now I am bent to know
By the worst means, the worst. For mine own good
All causes shall give way. I am in blood
Stepped in so far that, should I wade no more,
Returning were as tedious as go o'er.

Lady Macbeth: You lack the season of all natures, sleep.

Macbeth: Come, we'll to sleep.
We are yet but young in deed.

They leave

---

[1] paid as a spy

Act 4 Scene 1

A desolate place near Forres

Thunder. The three Witches come in

First Witch: Thrice the brinded cat hath mewed.

Second Witch: Thrice, and once the hedge-pig whined.

Third Witch: Harpier cries 'Tis time, 'tis time.

First Witch: Round about the cauldron go,
In the poisoned entrails throw.
Toad that under cold stone
Days and nights has thirty-one
Sweltered venom sleeping got,
Boil thou first i' th' charmèd pot.

All: Double, double, toil and trouble,
Fire burn, and cauldron bubble.

Second Witch: Fillet of a fenny snake,
In the cauldron boil and bake.
Eye of newt and toe of frog,
Wool of bat and tongue of dog,
Adder's fork and blind-worm's sting,
Lizard's leg and owlet's wing,
For a charm of powerful trouble,
Like a hell-broth boil and bubble.

All: Double, double, toil and trouble,
Fire burn, and cauldron bubble.

Third Witch: Scale of dragon, tooth of wolf,
Witches' mummy[1], maw and gulf
Of the ravined salt-sea shark,
Root of hemlock digged i' th' dark.

All: Double, double, toil and trouble,
Fire burn, and cauldron bubble.

Second Witch: Cool it with a baboon's blood,
Then the charm is firm and good.
By the pricking of my thumbs,
Something wicked this way comes.

Macbeth enters

---

[1] potion made from a mummy

Macbeth: How now, you secret, black, and midnight hags,
What is 't you do?

All Witches: A deed without a name.

Macbeth: I conjure you by that which you profess,
Howe'er you come to know it, answer me
To what I ask you.

First Witch: Speak.

Second Witch: Demand.

Third Witch: We'll answer.

First Witch: Say if thou'dst rather hear it from our mouths
Or from our masters.

Macbeth: Call 'em, let me see 'em.

First Witch: Pour in sow's blood that hath eaten
Her nine farrow; grease that's sweaten
From the murderer's gibbet throw
Into the flame.

All Witches: Come high or low,
Thyself and office deftly show.

Thunder. The First Apparition is a head with a helmet on

Macbeth: Tell me, thou unknown power—

First Witch: He knows thy thought.
Hear his speech, but say thou naught.

1st Apparition: Macbeth, Macbeth, Macbeth, beware Macduff,
Beware the Thane of Fife. Dismiss me. Enough.

The First Apparition disappears

Macbeth: Whate'er thou art, for thy good caution thanks.
Thou hast harped my fear aright. But one word more—

First Witch: He will not be commanded. Here's another,
More potent[1] than the first.

Thunder. The Second Apparition is a child covered in blood

2nd Apparition: Macbeth, Macbeth, Macbeth.

Macbeth: Had I three ears I'd hear thee.

---

[1] powerful

The Public Theater, New York, © Michal Daniel

2nd Apparition: Be bloody, bold, and resolute. Laugh to scorn
The power of man, for none of woman born
Shall harm Macbeth.

The Second Apparition disappears

Macbeth: Then live, Macduff—what need I fear of thee?
But yet I'll make assurance double sure,
And take a bond of fate thou shalt not live,
That I may tell pale-hearted fear it lies,
And sleep in spite of thunder.

Thunder. The Third Apparition is a child wearing a crown, with a tree in his hand

What is this
That rises like the issue of a king?

All Witches: Listen, but speak not to 't.

3rd Apparition: Be lion-mettled, proud, and take no care
Who chafes, who frets, or where conspirers are.
Macbeth shall never vanquished be until
Great Birnam Wood to high Dunsinane Hill
Shall come against him.

The Third Apparition disappears

Macbeth: That will never be.
Who can impress the forest, bid the tree
Unfix his earth-bound root? Yet my heart
Throbs to know one thing. Tell me, if your art
Can tell so much, shall Banquo's issue ever
Reign in this kingdom?

All Witches: Seek to know no more.

Macbeth: I will be satisfied. Deny me this,
And an eternal curse fall on you! Let me know.

The cauldron disappears. There is the sound of trumpets

First Witch: Show.

Second Witch: Show.

Third Witch: Show.

All Witches: Show his eyes and grieve his heart,
Come like shadows, so depart.

Eight Kings appear, the last one with a mirror in his hand. Banquo's Ghost follows them in.

Macbeth: Thou art too like the spirit of Banquo. Down!
Thy crown does sear mine eyeballs. And thy hair,
Thou other gold-bound brow, is like the first.
A third is like the former. Filthy hags,
Why do you show me this?—A fourth? Start, eyes!
What, will the line stretch out to th' crack of doom?
Another yet? A seventh? I'll see no more—
And yet the eighth appears, who bears a glass
Which shows me many more;
Horrible sight! Now I see 'tis true,

For the blood-boltered Banquo smiles upon me,
And points at them for his.

The Kings and Banquo's Ghost leave.

What, is this so?

First Witch: Ay, sir, all this is so. But why
Stands Macbeth thus amazedly?

The Witches vanish

Macbeth: Where are they? Gone? Let this pernicious[1] hour
Stand aye accursèd in the calendar.
Come in, without there.

Lennox comes in

Lennox: What's your grace's will?

Macbeth: Saw you the weird sisters?

Lennox: No, my lord.

Macbeth: Came they not by you?

Lennox: No, indeed, my lord.

Macbeth: Infected be the air whereon they ride,
And damned all those that trust them. I did hear
The galloping of horse. Who was 't came by?

Lennox: 'Tis two or three, my lord, that bring you word
Macduff is fled to England.

Macbeth: Fled to England?

Lennox: Ay, my good lord.

Macbeth: *(To himself)* From this moment
The very firstlings of my heart shall be
The firstlings of my hand. And even now,
To crown my thoughts with acts, be it thought and done:
The castle of Macduff I will surprise,
Seize upon Fife, give to th' edge o' th' sword
His wife, his babes, and all unfortunate souls
That trace him in his line. No boasting like a fool;
This deed I'll do before this purpose cool.

They leave

---

[1] harmful, deadly

Act 4 Scene 2

Macduff's castle in Fife

Lady Macduff comes in with her Son and Ross

Lady Macduff: What had he done to make him fly the land?

Ross: You must have patience, madam.

Lady Macduff: He had none.
His flight was madness. When our actions do not,
Our fears do make us traitors.

Ross: You know not
Whether it was his wisdom or his fear.

Lady Macduff: Wisdom—to leave his wife, to leave his babes,
His mansion, and his titles in a place
From whence himself does fly? He loves us not,
He wants the natural touch.

Ross: My dearest coz,
I pray you school yourself. But for your husband,
He is noble, wise, judicious, and best knows
The fits o' th' season. *(To the boy)* My pretty cousin,
Blessing upon you!

Lady Macduff: Fathered he is, and yet he's fatherless.

Ross: I am so much a fool, should I stay longer
It would be my disgrace and your discomfort.
I take my leave at once.

He leaves

Lady Macduff: Sirrah, your father's dead,
And what will you do now?

Son: If he were dead you'd weep for him. If you would not, it were a good sign that I should quickly have a new father.

Lady Macduff: Poor prattler, how thou talk'st!

A Messenger comes in

Messenger: Bless you, fair dame. I am not to you known,
I doubt[1] some danger does approach you nearly.
Be not found here. Hence with your little ones!
Heaven preserve you. I dare abide no longer.

The Messenger runs off

Lady Macduff: Whither should I fly?
I have done no harm. But I remember now
I am in this earthly world, where to do harm
Is often laudable, to do good sometime
Accounted dangerous folly.

The Murderers come in

What are these faces?

Murderer: Where is your husband?

Lady Macduff: I hope in no place so unsanctified
Where such as thou mayst find him.

Murderer: He's a traitor.

Son: Thou liest, thou shag-haired villain.

Murderer: *(stabbing him)* What, you egg!
Young fry of treachery!

Son: He has killed me, mother.
Run away, I pray you.

Lady Macduff runs off followed by the Murderers

[1] suspect

Act 4 Scene 3

King Edward's palace in England

The Narrators enter

Narrator 2: *(Visibly upset)* I can't believe that anyone would kill an innocent child like that!

Narrator 1: It is a terrible thing for the whole of Scotland to be ruled by an evil tyrant.

Narrator 2: But why didn't Macduff stay?

Narrator 1: He's in England, at the court of the holy English king, Edward. He wants Malcolm to return to Scotland.

Narrator 2: How will Malcolm know that he can trust Macduff? He could be spying for Macbeth.

Narrator 1: He will have to test Macduff before he can trust him. Malcolm is going to pretend to be even worse than Macbeth.

The Narrators step aside. Malcolm and Macduff come in, deep in conversation

Macduff: Each new morn
New widows howl, new orphans cry, new sorrows
Strike heaven on the face that it resounds
As if it felt with Scotland.

Malcolm: This tyrant, whose sole name blisters our tongues,
Was once thought honest. You have loved him well.

Macduff: I am not treacherous.

Malcolm: But Macbeth is.
Though all things foul would wear the brows of grace,
Yet grace must still look so.

Macduff: I have lost my hopes.

Malcolm: Why in that rawness left you wife and child,
Those precious motives, those strong knots of love,
Without leave-taking? You may be rightly just,
Whatever I shall think.

Macduff: Bleed, bleed, poor country!
Great tyranny, lay thou thy basis sure,

For goodness dare not check thee. Fare thee well, lord.
I would not be the villain that thou think'st
For the whole space that's in the tyrant's grasp,
And the rich East to boot.

Malcolm: Be not offended.
I speak not as in absolute fear of you.
I think our country sinks beneath the yoke.
It weeps, it bleeds, and each new day a gash
Is added to her wounds. I think withal
There would be hands uplifted in my right,
And here from gracious England have I offer
Of goodly thousands. But for all this,
When I shall tread upon the tyrant's head,
Or wear it on my sword, yet my poor country
Shall have more vices than it had before,
More suffer, and more sundry ways, than ever,
By him that shall succeed.

Macduff: What should he be?

Malcolm: It is myself I mean, in whom I know
All the particulars of vice so grafted
That when they shall be opened, black Macbeth
Will seem as pure as snow, and the poor state
Esteem him as a lamb, being compared
With my confineless harms.

Macduff: Not in the legions
Of horrid hell can come a devil more damned
In evils to top Macbeth.

Malcolm: The king-becoming graces,
As justice, verity, temp'rance, stableness,
Bounty, perseverance, mercy, lowliness,
Devotion, patience, courage, fortitude,
I have no relish of them, but abound
In the division of each several crime,
Acting it many ways. Nay, had I power I should
Pour the sweet milk of concord into hell,
Uproar the universal peace, confound
All unity on earth.

Macduff: O Scotland, Scotland!

Malcolm: If such a one be fit to govern, speak.
I am as I have spoken.

Macduff: Fit to govern?
No, not to live. O nation miserable,
With an untitled tyrant bloody-sceptred,
When shalt thou see thy wholesome days again?
Fare thee well,
These evils thou repeat'st upon thyself
Hath banished me from Scotland.

Malcolm: Macduff, this noble passion,
Child of integrity, hath from my soul
Wiped the black scruples, reconciled my thoughts
To thy good truth and honour. For even now
I put myself to thy direction and
Unspeak mine own detraction, here abjure
The taints and blames I laid upon myself
For strangers to my nature. What I am truly
Is thine and my poor country's to command,
Now we'll together; and the chance of goodness
Be like our warranted quarrel!—Why are you silent?

Macduff: Such welcome and unwelcome things at once
'Tis hard to reconcile.

Ross comes in

See who comes here.
My ever gentle cousin, welcome hither.
Stands Scotland where it did?

Ross: Alas, poor country,
Almost afraid to know itself. It cannot
Be called our mother, but our grave.

Macduff: How does my wife?

Ross: Why, well.

Macduff: And all my children?

Ross: Well, too.

Macduff: The tyrant has not battered at their peace?

Ross: No, they were well at peace when I did leave 'em.

Macduff: Be not a niggard of your speech. How goes 't?

Ross: Now is the time of help. *(To Malcolm)* Your eye in Scotland
Would create soldiers, make our women fight
To doff their dire distresses.

Malcolm: Be 't their comfort
We are coming thither.

Ross: Would I could answer
This comfort with the like. But I have words
That would be howled out in the desert air
Where hearing should not latch them.

Macduff: Keep it not from me; quickly let me have it.

Ross: Your castle is surprised, your wife and babes
Savagely slaughtered.

Malcolm: Merciful heaven!
(To Macduff)
What, man, ne'er pull your hat upon your brows.
Give sorrow words.

Macduff: My children too?

Ross: Wife, children, servants, all
That could be found.

Macduff: And I must be from thence!
My wife killed too?

Ross: I have said.

Malcolm: Be comforted.
Let's make us medicines of our great revenge
To cure this deadly grief.

Macduff: He has no children. All my pretty ones?
Did you say all? O hell-kite! All?
What, all my pretty chickens and their dam
At one fell swoop?

Malcolm: Dispute it like a man.

Macduff: I shall do so,

But I must also feel it as a man.
I cannot but remember such things were
That were most precious to me. Did heaven look on
And would not take their part? Sinful Macduff,
They were all struck for thee. Heaven rest them now.

Malcolm: Be this the whetstone of your sword. Let grief
Convert to anger: blunt not the heart, enrage it.

Macduff: O, I could play the woman with mine eyes
And braggart with my tongue! But gentle heavens
Cut short all intermission. Front to front
Bring thou this fiend of Scotland and myself.
Within my sword's length set him. If he scape,
Heaven forgive him too.

Malcolm: This tune goes manly.
Come, go we to the King. Our power is ready;
Our lack is nothing but our leave. Macbeth
Is ripe for shaking. Receive what cheer you may:
The night is long that never finds the day.

They leave

Narrator 1: So Malcolm and Macduff will lead an army of English and Scottish soldiers against Macbeth.

Narrator 2: I knew that they'd get help from King Edward of England. He is such a good man that they say he can heal the sick!

Narrator 1: It looks more hopeful for Scotland now!

Angela Bassett as Lady Macbeth, Public Theater, New York, © Michal Daniel

Act 5 Scene 1

A room in Dunsinane, Macbeth's strongest castle

Lady Macbeth's Gentlewoman comes in with a Doctor

Doctor: I have two nights watched with you, but can perceive no truth in your report. When was it she last walked?

Gentlewoman: Since his majesty went into the field I have seen her rise from her bed, throw her nightgown upon her, unlock her closet, take forth paper, fold it, write upon't, read it, afterwards seal it, and again return to bed, yet all this while in a most fast sleep.

Doctor: A great perturbation in nature, to receive at once the benefit of sleep and do the effects of watching.

Lady Macbeth comes in carrying a candle

Lo you, here she comes. This is her very guise, and, upon my life, fast asleep. Observe her. Stand close.

Doctor: How came she by that light?

Gentlewoman: Why, it stood by her. She has light by her continually. 'Tis her command.

Doctor: You see her eyes are open.

Gentlewoman: Ay, but their sense are shut.

Doctor: What is it she does now? Look how she rubs her hands.

Gentlewoman: It is an accustomed action with her, to seem thus washing her hands. I have known her continue in this a quarter of an hour.

Lady Macbeth: Yet here's a spot.

Doctor: Hark, she speaks.

Lady Macbeth: Out, damned spot; out, I say. One, two,—why, then 'tis time to do 't. Hell is murky. Fie, my lord, fie, a soldier and afeard? What need we fear who knows it when none can call our power to account? Yet who would have thought the old man to have had so much blood in him?

Doctor: Do you mark that?

Lady Macbeth: The Thane of Fife had a wife. Where is she now? What, will these hands ne'er be clean? No more o' that, my lord, no more o' that. You mar all with this starting.

Doctor: Go to, go to. You have known what you should not.

Gentlewoman: She has spoke what she should not, I am sure of that. Heaven knows what she has known.

Lady Macbeth: Here's the smell of the blood still. All the perfumes of Arabia will not sweeten this little hand. Oh!

Doctor: What a sigh is there! The heart is sorely charged.

Gentlewoman: I would not have such a heart in my bosom for the dignity of the whole body.

Doctor: This disease is beyond my practice.

Lady Macbeth: Wash your hands, put on your nightgown, look not so pale. I tell you yet again, Banquo's buried. He cannot come out on 's grave.

Doctor: Even so?

Lady Macbeth: To bed, to bed. There's knocking at the gate. Come, come, come, come, give me your hand. What's done cannot be undone. To bed, to bed, to bed.

Lady Macbeth goes out

Doctor: Foul whisp'rings are abroad. Unnatural deeds
Do breed unnatural troubles; infected minds
To their deaf pillows will discharge their secrets.
More needs she the divine than the physician.
God, God forgive us all! Look after her.
Remove from her the means of all annoyance,
And still keep eyes upon her. So, good night.
I think, but dare not speak.

Gentlewoman: Good night, good doctor.

They leave.

Angela Bassett as Lady Macbeth, Public Theater, New York, © Michal Daniel

Act 5 Scene 2

Open country in Scotland

Ross and Lennox, come in with Soldiers, a drummer and flags. The Narrators are amongst the soldiers.

Narrator 2: I've been thinking about this army, is it any use? From what the witches said, it doesn't sound like anyone can defeat Macbeth.

Narrator 1: Yes, but remember what Banquo said about the witches telling the truth to deceive people.

Lennox: The English power is near, led on by Malcolm,
His uncle Siward, and the good Macduff.
Revenges burn in them.

Ross: Near Birnam Wood
Shall we well meet them. That way are they coming.

Lennox: What does the tyrant?

Ross: Great Dunsinane he strongly fortifies.
Some say he's mad, others that lesser hate him
Do call it valiant fury, but for certain
He cannot buckle his distempered cause
Within the belt of rule.

Lennox: Now does he feel
His secret murders sticking on his hands.
Those he commands move only in command,
Nothing in love. Now does he feel his title
Hang loose about him, like a giant's robe
Upon a dwarfish thief.

Ross: Well, march we on
To give obedience where 'tis truly owed.

Lennox: Make we our march towards Birnam.

They march out.

Act 5 Scene 3

Inside Dunsinane Castle

Macbeth comes in with the Doctor and some Servants

Macbeth: Bring me no more reports. Let them fly all.
Till Birnam Wood remove to Dunsinane
I cannot taint with fear. What's the boy Malcolm?
Was he not born of woman? The spirits that know
All mortal consequences have pronounced me thus:
"Fear not, Macbeth. No man that's born of woman
Shall e'er have power upon thee."

A Servant comes in

The devil damn thee black, thou cream-faced loon!
Where got'st thou that goose look?

Servant: There is ten thousand—

Macbeth: Geese, villain?

Servant: Soldiers, sir.

Macbeth: Go prick thy face and over-red thy fear,
Thou lily-livered boy. What soldiers, patch?
Death of thy soul, those linen cheeks of thine
Are counsellors to fear. What soldiers, whey-face?

Servant: The English force, so please you.

Macbeth: Take thy face hence.

The Servant leaves

I have lived long enough. My way of life
Is fall'n into the sere,[1] the yellow leaf,
And that which should accompany old age,
As honour, love, obedience, troops of friends,
I must not look to have, but in their stead
Curses, not loud but deep, mouth-honour, breath
Which the poor heart would fain deny and dare not.
Seyton!

Seyton comes in

---

[1] dried up, withered phase of a plant's life

Seyton: What's your gracious pleasure?

Macbeth: What news more?

Seyton: All is confirmed, my lord, which was reported.

Macbeth: I'll fight till from my bones my flesh be hacked.
Give me my armour.

Seyton: 'Tis not needed yet.

Macbeth: I'll put it on.
Send out more horses. Skirr the country round.
Hang those that talk of fear. Give me mine armour.
How does your patient, doctor?

As Macbeth speaks, his servants help him into his armour.

Doctor: Not so sick, my lord,
As she is troubled with thick-coming fancies
That keep her from her rest.

Macbeth: Cure her of that.
Canst thou not minister to a mind diseased,
Pluck from the memory a rooted sorrow,
Raze out the written troubles of the brain,
And with some sweet oblivious antidote
Cleanse the fraught bosom of that perilous stuff
Which weighs upon the heart?

Doctor: Therein the patient
Must minister to himself.

Macbeth: Throw physic to the dogs; I'll none of it.
Come, put mine armour on. Give me my staff.
Seyton, send out. Doctor, the thanes fly from me.
(To the servant) Come sir, dispatch[1].
I will not be afraid of death and bane
Till Birnam Forest come to Dunsinane.

They all leave

---

[1] hurry

Act 5 Scene 4

Near Birnam Wood

Enter Malcolm, Lennox, Macduff and Soldiers

Malcolm: What wood is this before us?

Lennox: The wood of Birnam.

Malcolm: Let every soldier hew him down a bough
And bear 't before him. Thereby shall we shadow
The numbers of our host, and make discovery
Err in report of us.

Lennox: We learn no other but the confident tyrant
Keeps still in Dunsinane, and will endure
Our setting down before 't.

Malcolm: 'Tis his main hope,
For none serve with him but constrainèd things,
Whose hearts are absent too.

Macduff: Let our just censures
Attend the true event, and put we on
Industrious soldiership.

They march out

Act 5 Scene 5

Inside Dunsinane Castle

Macbeth, comes in with Seyton, soldiers, a drummer and flags

Macbeth: Hang out our banners on the outward walls.
The cry is still "They come." Our castle's strength
Will laugh a siege to scorn. Here let them lie
Till famine and the ague[1] eat them up.

There is the sound of a cry from inside the castle

What is that noise?

Seyton: It is the cry of women, my good lord.

---

[1] fever

He leaves

Macbeth: I have almost forgot the taste of fears.
The time has been my senses would have cooled
To hear a night-shriek, and my fell of hair
Would at a dismal treatise rouse and stir
As life were in 't. I have supped full with horrors.

Seyton returns

Wherefore was that cry?

Seyton: The Queen, my lord, is dead.

Macbeth: She should have died hereafter.
There would have been a time for such a word.
Tomorrow, and tomorrow, and tomorrow,
Creeps in this petty pace from day to day
To the last syllable of recorded time,
And all our yesterdays have lighted fools
The way to dusty death. Out, out, brief candle!
Life's but a walking shadow, a poor player
That struts and frets his hour upon the stage,
And then is heard no more. It is a tale
Told by an idiot, full of sound and fury,
Signifying nothing.

A Messenger comes in

Thou com'st to use thy tongue: thy story quickly.

Messenger: Gracious my lord,
I should report that which I say I saw,
But know not how to do it.

Macbeth: Well, say, sir.

Messenger: As I did stand my watch upon the hill,
I looked toward Birnam, and anon, methought,
The wood began to move.

Macbeth: Liar and slave!

Messenger: Let me endure your wrath if 't be not so.
Within this three mile may you see it coming.
I say, a moving grove.

Macbeth: I pall in resolution[1], and begin
To doubt th' equivocation[2] of the fiend,
That lies like truth. "Fear not till Birnam Wood
Do come to Dunsinane"—and now a wood
Comes toward Dunsinane. Arm, arm, and out.
If this which he avouches does appear
There is nor flying hence nor tarrying here.
I 'gin to be aweary of the sun,
And wish th' estate o' th' world were now undone.
Ring the alarum bell. Blow wind, come wrack,
At least we'll die with harness on our back.

They go out

The Public Theater, New York, © Michal Daniel

[1] lose confidence and determination

[2] double talk

Act 5 Scene 6

Outside Dunsinane Castle

All the action which follows takes place around the castle as people search for each other in the heat of battle.

Malcolm and Macduff come in, with a drummer and flags and soldiers carrying branches.

Malcolm: Now near enough. Your leafy screens throw down,
And show like those you are.

Macduff: Make all our trumpets speak, give them all breath,
Those clamorous harbingers of blood and death.

They leave as the trumpets start

Macbeth comes in

Macbeth: They have tied me to a stake. I cannot fly,
But bear-like I must fight the course. What's he
That was not born of woman? Such a one
Am I to fear, or none.

A soldier enters and starts to fight with Macbeth

Thou wast born of woman.
But swords I smile at, weapons laugh to scorn,
Brandished by man that's of a woman born.

They go off fighting.

Macduff enters

Macduff: That way the noise is. Tyrant, show thy face!
If thou be'est slain and with no stroke of mine,
My wife and children's ghosts will haunt me still.

Macbeth comes in, still looking back at where he has killed the soldier

Macbeth: Why should I play the Roman fool, and die
On mine own sword? Whiles I see lives, the gashes
Do better upon them.

Macduff: Turn, hell-hound, turn.

Macbeth: Of all men else I have avoided thee.
But get thee back. My soul is too much charged
With blood of thine already.

Macduff: I have no words;
My voice is in my sword, thou bloodier villain
Than terms can give thee out.

They fight

Macbeth: Thou losest labour.
I bear a charmèd life, which must not yield
To one of woman born.

Macduff: Despair thy charm,
And let the angel whom thou still hast served
Tell thee, Macduff was from his mother's womb
Untimely ripped.

Macbeth: Accursèd be that tongue that tells me so,
For it hath cowed my better part of man;
And be these juggling fiends no more believed,
That palter with us in a double sense,
That keep the word of promise to our ear
And break it to our hope. I'll not fight with thee.

Macduff: Then yield thee, coward,
And live to be the show and gaze o' th' time.
We'll have thee as our rarer monsters are,
Painted upon a pole, and underwrit
"Here may you see the tyrant."

Macbeth: I will not yield
To kiss the ground before young Malcolm's feet,
And to be baited with the rabble's curse.
Though Birnam Wood be come to Dunsinane,
And thou opposed being of no woman born,
Yet I will try the last. Before my body
I throw my warlike shield. Lay on, Macduff,
And damned be him that first cries "Hold, enough!"

They fight fiercely until Macbeth is killed. Macduff drags the body away

Act 5 Scene 7

Inside Dunsinane Castle

Trumpets. Malcolm comes in with Lords and Soldiers, a drummer and flags.

Malcolm: I would the friends we miss were safe arrived.

Macduff comes in carrying the head of Macbeth.

Macduff: Hail, King, for so thou art. Behold where stands
Th' usurper's cursèd head. Hail, King of Scotland!

Lords: Hail, King of Scotland!

Fanfare

Malcolm: We shall not spend a large expense of time
Before we reckon with your several loves
And make us even with you. What's more to do
Which would be planted newly with the time–
As calling home our exiled friends abroad,
That fled the snares of watchful tyranny,
Producing forth the cruel ministers
Of this dead butcher and his fiend-like queen,
Who, as 'tis thought, by self and violent hands
Took off her life — this and what needful else
That calls upon us, by the grace of Grace
We will perform in measure, time, and place.
So thanks to all at once, and to each one,
Whom we invite to see us crowned at Scone.

There is a fanfare and they all leave.

Commonwealth Shakespeare Company, © Ryan Maxwell

Published by Carel Press Ltd, 4 Hewson Street, Carlisle, Tel 01228 538928. info@carelpress.com
www.carelpress.com

Reprinted October 2000, 2001, 2003. Reprinted in colour 2010, 2014

Printed by Interpress, Budapest

CIP Data:
Shakespeare, William, 1564-1616
Macbeth: the Shorter Shakespeare
1 Macbeth, King of Scotland, d1057 - drama
I Title II Shepherd, Christine E.
822.3'3

ISBN 978 1 872365 59 6

Macbeth

- An indispensable introduction to Shakespeare
- Ideal for both study and performance
- Makes the play enjoyable and accessible to all young people

The best selling Shorter Shakespeare series provides shortened versions in the original language, with links by modern narrators.

See them all at
www.shortershakespeare.co.uk

"We are really pleased with the Shorter Shakespeare... The pupils have thoroughly enjoyed it and have been very enthusiastic."

A. MacDonald, Kingussie High School

CAREL Inspire Learning
www.carelpress.co.uk

ISBN 978-1-872365-59-6

9 781872 365596

THE BRISTOL BUS BOYCOTT: A FIGHT FOR RACIAL JUSTICE

SANDRA A. AGARD

CHELLIE CARROLL

Published by Collins
An imprint of HarperCollins*Publishers*

The News Building
1 London Bridge Street
London SE1 9GF
UK

Macken House,
39/40 Mayor Street Upper,
Dublin 1, DO1 C9W8,
Ireland

10 9 8 7 6 5 4 3

ISBN 978-0-00-842457-2

British Library Cataloguing-in-Publication Data
A catalogue record for this publication is available from the British Library.

Author: Sandra A. Agard
Illustrators: Chellie Carroll (Advocate Art) and
Collaborate Agency Ltd
Reading ideas author: Gill Matthews
Publisher: Lizzie Catford
Commissioning and development editor: Leilani Sparrow
Product managers: Jennifer Hall and Sarah Thomas
In-house content editors: Roisin Leahy and Hatty Skinner
Project manager: Emily Hooton
Copyeditor: Sally Byford
Proofreader: Gaynor Spry
Picture researchers: Roisin Leahy and Sophie Hartley
Typesetter: 2Hoots Publishing Services Ltd
Cover designer: 2Hoots Publishing Services Ltd
Production controller: Katharine Willard

Printed and Bound in the UK using 100% Renewable Electricity at Martins the Printers Ltd

Acknowledgements
The publishers gratefully acknowledge the permission granted to reproduce the copyright material in this book. Every effort has been made to trace copyright holders and to obtain their permission for the use of copyright material. The publishers will gladly receive any information enabling them to rectify any error or omission at the first opportunity.

pp2–3 Dom Slike/Alamy Stock Photo, p4 Robert Proctor/ Alamy Stock Photo, pp4–5 Mirrorpix/Reach Plc (photo courtesy Bristol Libraries), p8 Chronicle/Alamy Stock Photo, p9 IWM/Getty Images, p10 Bill Orchard/ Shutterstock, p11 Daily Mail/Shutterstock, pp18–19 Horace Cort/AP/Shutterstock, p20 Science History Images/Alamy Stock Photo, p21 Don Cravens/Getty Images, p22 Mirrorpix/Reach Plc (photo courtesy Bristol Libraries), pp30–31 Grzegorz Burakovsky/Shutterstock, p36 Mirrorpix/Reach Plc (photo courtesy Bristol Libraries), p37t Mirrorpix/Getty Images, p37b History and Art Collection/Alamy Stock Photo, p42l Mirrorpix/ Reach Plc (photo courtesy Bristol Libraries), p42r Source: Vernon Samuels, p43 Photo by Tim Browning, p44 Steve Taylor ARPS/Alamy Stock Photo